Let's Do It!

by

Catherine Forde

In fond memory of my stunt boy

First published in 2011 in Great Britain by
Barrington Stoke Ltd
18 Walker Street, Edinburgh, EH3 7LP

www.barringtonstoke.co.uk

ISBN: 978-1-84299-941-7

Printed in China by Leo

Contents

Chapter 1
Let's Do It! Do It, Dudes!

"Come *on!*" said Ben.

"Are we going in or what?" said Alan.

"Let's do it! Do it, Dudes!"

That was me. I'm Mel. Ben and Alan are my two mates.

The three of us were standing outside a class-room.

Being outside class-rooms is normal for Ben and Alan and me. Almost every day it happens to *one* of us. Teachers put us outside their doors for ...

Well ...

You know ...

Doing stuff we think's funny. But teachers don't.

E.g.: Leaving rude drawings on the board.

Turning desks the wrong way round and upside down.

Bringing hamsters, and mice, and kittens into class in our school-bags.

Then letting them out in the middle of a lesson, etc, etc ...

What was not normal today was that all three of us were outside a class-room *wanting* to go *in*. And to do something that was not a prank. And during lunch hour too.

But here we were. We'd been outside the class-room for *ages*. We'd stood there whispering daft things to each other like:

Me: Look. Just go in.

Alan: But what's Brad going to do when he sees us?

Ben: Nothing.

Me: Brad's only a teacher. It's not like he's *dangerous*.

Alan: OK then, you go first.

Ben: No, *you* go first.

Alan: I *always* go first.

If you heard us you would think we were three sissy, wet wimps. Scared of a teacher. But we *so* are not. *I* am no sissy, wet wimp. No way. And I am *so* not scared of Brad.

That was why I gave Ben and Alan the signal. *Our* signal. I chanted, "*Let's do it! Do it, Dudes!*" and I punched my heart with my fist.

One of us always has to say that. It's our call to battle. On that signal, we stop messing around. We just go.

Do or die.

Game on.

So when Alan and Ben heard me say, *"Let's do it! Do it, Dudes!"* they both shoved me in the back.

"Go! Go! Go!" they yelled, as if they were chucking me out of a helicopter into a war zone.

Or squeezing me into Ben's dishwasher covered in HP sauce because I'm the smallest. (Like they did last week to prank Ben's mum. Oooooh. Did she get a fright when she went to load it up? She still can't see the funny side.)

You would *not* think they were just pushing me against the door to Brad's geography room.

Ben and Alan pushed so hard that I crashed into the class-room. The door flung back. It opened so hard and so wide it almost ripped off its hinges.

Bang!

The door slammed into a wall with maps all over it. I don't have a clue what the maps were for. Why would I? Geography is for snoozing in, not learning stuff.

Crash!

A plastic tub fell off a shelf. It sent hundreds of pencils rolling all over the floor.

"Eeeek!"

Three pupils, who'd been watching a black and white film, all jumped up from their seats at the same time.

Clang!

The chairs their bums had been parked on hit the floor.

One of the pupils fell off her chair and hit the floor too. I couldn't see who she was because her skirt flipped up over her face when she fell. But I do know she was wearing spotty pants. B-i-i-i-i-i-g spotty pants.

"O.M.G. We might have known!" The two other pupils in Brad's room giggled.

They both had their hands pressed to their cheeks, but I could tell it was Jasper and Robbie. No one else in this school wears silver scarves. Or plucks their eyebrows so thin. Girl or boy.

"What is this, Sir?" Jasper peeked through his fingers. He giggled his question to the fourth person in the room.

That person was Brad, the teacher, and he did not giggle back at Jasper. Brad was storming up the class-room. He looked like a bull on the charge; head down, steam puffing out his ears.

OK, I made that last bit up. No steam. But he did look pretty upset.

Brad's arms were waving about mad. And boy, oh boy! Was he shouting! At me and Alan and Ben.

"Out! Out! Out!" Brad shouted.

"But, Sir," I said.

"Please, Sir," Alan added.

"We only want to join your – " That was Ben.

"Out!!!!! Get. Out!!!!!!!!!!!"

Brad had charged up to the door now. His waving arms shooed the three of us out.

"Not welcome here, my friends," Brad yelled.

Then he banged the door shut in our faces.

Chapter 2

YOUR FILM CLUB NEEDS YOU!

"Not fair," said Ben.

"Not on," said Alan.

"'*Not welcome here, my friends.*'" That was me. Doing Brad's stupid voice. Copying him.

"Not over," I added in my own voice.

But I didn't really know what to do now.

The three of us were stuck outside Brad's class. And we were still looking at him. Not looking at the *real* Brad any more. *Our* Brad.

Now we were looking at pictures of his face. It was on two posters stuck to the door.

On the first poster, Brad was giving a stupid big fat cheesy smile. And he was winking. Like he was a great teacher. Good fun. Good temper. Good sport. Good guy.

Under Brad's face, you could count at least three wobbly chins.

"Look at that. More chins than hair," Ben said.

The few wisps of hair Brad had left were grown out long. This was so Brad could comb them up then lay them across the top of his bald head. If Brad thought that little trick would hide the fact that he was going bald, it didn't work. It just made poor Brad look sad, yet funny. So sad, yet funny that Ben and Alan and I once made a secret close-up film of his head.

Well, it *was* a secret film, till I called it "Comb Over" and banged it up on YouTube. That could be one of the many reasons why Brad hates me and Ben and Alan.

Anyway, on one poster on Brad's door, his face was photo-shopped onto that famous old advert.

You'll know it.

It's of that army bloke with the funny tash. Lord Kitchen or something? His finger points out the poster. Underneath his face it says:

Your country needs YOU!

You know the advert I mean? Mr Swigg, my crusty history teacher told us you saw that poster everywhere during the First World War. It was put up to make people join the Forces and then get themselves killed.

I nearly got myself killed when I asked Mr Swigg if *he* went off and joined the Army when he saw the poster in The Olden Days. Then I asked him if he met my great-granddad in the trenches.

I thought that was a bang sharp history question. About trenches and that. But Mr Swigg made me write out,

"A spell in the army would wipe the grin off my face!"

a thousand times.

So that's how I remember the Lord Kitchen poster. And when I saw the photo-shopped copy of the Lord Kitchen poster on Brad's door I remember how the real poster said:

Your country needs YOU

Not

St Mark's <u>FILM CLUB</u> needs YOU!

Which is what Brad's poster said. And Lord Kitchen's poster didn't say:

All Welcome

in silver pen.

But Brad's did. Robbie and Jason must have written the "All Welcome" in. They just love all things silver: silver scarves, silver eye-liner, silver bags, silver belts ... Me, Ben and Alan call them the Silver Sisters. Robbie and Jason think we're a scream.

Chapter 3

Brad

"Look." Alan smacked his hand off Brad's picture. "'*All welcome,*'" he read out loud. "So why can't we join Film Club?" he said.

"We want to make films," said Ben.

"Brad doesn't trust us, that's why." I shook my head.

I pressed my thumb on the second poster. Brad's face was on it too. This time his ugly mug was photo-shopped into a shot from an action movie. *Troy.* And there was *our* baldy Brad. He was wearing a leather tunic and carrying a spear. He had long, flowing hair and the body and muscles of the film-star Brad.

Do you need a clue to know who the other Brad is?

If I tell you he's buff and A-list, and has been up to plenty *how's-your-father* with that Angelina Jolie, do you know who I mean?

I'm talking *Fight Club* Brad Pitt. Who was married to Rachel off *Friends*. Film star Brad Pitt.

That Brad and our fatso Brad have the same surname. Can you believe it? Our Brad the crap geography teacher. Who lives with his mum, runs the Film Club, and won't let us join.

We call our Mr Pitt "Brad Pitt" but that's not his real name.

His real name is *Brian* Pitt.

And long ago, before Brad Pitt the major film star was a major film star, Mr Brian Pitt got called *far* worse names than Brad.

Now, I'm not going to say what the bad names were. But let me just tell you that my big brother Jack's class used to call Mr Pitt, "*Mr Pile Of Pitt*." And years ago, when my Jack went to St Mark's, Mr Pile Of Pitt used to run the Camera Club. Jack said he turned his geography cupboard into a dark room, and would lock his roly-poly self in there with his Camera Club boys. They'd print off snaps of pupils playing hockey and netball. But now that adults are not allowed to take random pictures of pupils any more in school, Brad's turned his dark room back into a cupboard. And he's started up a Film Club instead.

It runs *every* lunchtime. Me, Ben and Alan think that's because Brad's so sad, he has no teacher mates in the staffroom. So he runs Film Club to have somewhere to go. It shows old black and white films.

I know all this because the Silver Sisters sit with me, Ben and Alan in Art and give us all the goss. Robbie and Jason can't hang about the school yard at lunch because some kids don't like their silver scarves and the way they walk and giggle. So the Silver Sisters show up at Film Club every lunchtime too.

"It's not that we *like* the films Brad shows," Jason told me. "No way."

"And we don't like his film chat either," added Robbie. "No way. It's more bo-ring than his dress sense."

"And we don't want to learn how to work his fancy video camera," Jason yawned.

"We just do Film Club to see the swishy frocks in the old movies." Robbie gave me a twirl as if he was wearing a swishy frock himself. "They are to die for, Mel," he sighed.

"Totally to die for," Jason sighed and gave me a twirl too. "We just do Film Club to get ideas for the frocks *we'll* make one day."

Now, I bet you're thinking:

Why, oh why, are Stunt Dudes like Ben and Alan and Mel still outside Brad's room?

What do they care about his Film Club?

And why are they still looking at the poster that says:

We need new members

Bring your packed lunch.
Watch movies.
Make movies.

We were only there because of that one line on the poster.

And not the one that said, "**Bring your packed lunch**".

The line that said, "**Make movies**".

You see, that is what we love to do.

More than the Silver Sisters want to make frocks, we want to make movies.

And not just any movies. What we love are stunt movies. Movies where we leap off cars or trains or cows.

And throw ourselves into wet places.

And eat and drink crazy food.

(Like insects and belly cheese.)

And prank people.

Shock people.

And make people laugh.

Oh. And we want the chance to win ourselves a bit of cash.

There's this new internet show. *Cray-Zee Stunts* it's called. It's a kind of X-rated *You've Been Framed* without Harry Hill.

The new show needs home videos of Stunt Dudes like me and Ben and Alan doing our cray-zee stunts. And boy, oh, boy, do we want to make those films!

But we have one problem. We need a video camera. A good one, that zooms in and out.

It can't be too heavy. That's no use when you're climbing a fence. Or speeding away from security guards. Or farmers. Or the cops.

And we need one that won't smash if you drop it. Or if a dog bites it. Like the old one of Dad's I had till a guard dog bit it and it smashed.

(Sorry again, Dad. I'll pay you back if we ever get on *Cray-Zee Stunts*.)

And we like to film down toilets and drains and man-holes a lot. So we need a video that's waterproof. And one that won't smoke and heat up if it falls into the sea. Or into a cowpat. Like what happened to Alan's camera.

Well, not really Alan's.

Alan's brother's.

Alan's brother still doesn't know his camera's broken. Alan just dabbed off as much cow poo as he could. He put it back in its case. Stinky. And stuffed.

Since then we've made do with Ben's phone to film our stunts. But the sound and colour is rubbish.

So what we need is a quality video. Like the camera Brad has for his Film Club. The fancy one Jason and Robbie don't want to learn to use.

That very moment, as we were standing outside Brad's room, it was sitting on his desk.

"I can see it," Ben said. He was peeking through the window in Brad's door. "It's there. Just doing nothing."

"Going to waste," said Alan. He had his pen out and was drawing droopy boobs on Brad's leather tunic.

"I know," I said. "Small. Strong. Waterproof."

I wasn't talking about Brad when I said "Small. Strong. Waterproof." I was thinking about the camera and a film Brad had shown us last week in geography.

Brad didn't mean for us to see the film we ended up seeing. He had been going on and on and on about maps. How *interesting* they are. And how *interesting* the film was. About how to read a blooming map! Man, oh, man. I could not wait. But then, just as Brad was putting his memory stick into his computer, into class came another teacher. Oooh la la, it was Miss Wiggle.

"Bonjour, Meester Peet."

Miss Wiggle's a French teacher. And Miss Wiggle is not her real name.

Sad Brad has the horny hots for Miss Wiggle. Any time he sees her, his head glows bright red, and he keeps looking down her top.

Of course, our class starts doing wolf-whistles and talking dirty in French accents every time Brad tries to flirt. So that was why he steered Miss Wiggle into the corridor to chat her up, and our class ended up watching this *other* film by mistake.

The other film starred *our* Brad Pitt. In a red bobble hat, and a brown anorak and yellow nylon trousers. He was puffing up a hill in pissy rain, yak-yakking about weather and clouds and ...

Oh, who knows? It was so dull I nearly nodded off.

Until, on film, Brad took a tumble.

You didn't see it on camera. Just heard him grunt, "OOOF!" as his beer-belly hit the hill. Then you saw sky and grass and trees and sheep. They were right way up one minute, upside down the next.

Brad had dropped his video camera. It went rolling, and bouncing down the hill like a super-ball.

On film you heard Brad pant, "Help!" Then you heard his feet splosh and skid down the muddy hill as he chased the camera.

Of course, in class, every pupil was banging their desk and cheering.

"Enjoy your trip, Sir!"

"Boing! Boing!"

But not me. Or Ben. Or Alan. We were watching the screen.

There had been a splash, and now the video was filming water bubbles and stones. And then a plump pink hand came over the lens. That was Brad, grabbing the video out a stream. The next thing you saw was Brad's face in close up. There were two lines of snot running down his face like see-thru worms. Both in perfect focus.

"Testing. Testing," Brad was saying, as the video picked it up. Sound and vision. Clear as crystal. What a gadget!

So *that's* why me, Ben and Alan were so keen to join Film Club.

We wanted to get our hands on that tough little camera for our cray-zee stunts.

"But Brad's never going to let us near it. So what now?" said Ben. He was writing over the name-plate on Brad's door. Changing the "P" of Mr Pitt to ... what do YOU think?'

"*Well, you won't get any camera doing that, my friend.*'" I poked Ben. I was doing Brad's voice again. Saying the same thing Brad said when he came back into class after chatting up Miss Wiggle and saw us all watching the wrong film. "*It'll take a miracle before I trust you lot with anything in this school,*'" I added.

Then guess what?

Sister Fay came along the corridor, walking her springy walk.

Chapter 4
Sister Fay

"How are you all?" Sister Fay smiled. "Grand day, isn't it?"

Sister Fay always smiles. No matter what the weather. No matter who you are. No matter what you're doing. No matter what you've done. It's like the sun shines out her heart all day long. You could be Jack the Ripper, or Freddy Krueger and you'd still win a smile from Sister Fay.

I mean, there was Alan, doodling a big willy on Brad's poster. And Ben adding hairs to it, and Sister Fay was watching them both. Still she smiled.

"So Mr Pitt not letting you in there?" Sister Fay said.

"What's it look like?" said Ben.

A bit cheeky of Ben, I thought. After all, Sister Fay had caught us red-handed, doing bad things. If any other teacher found you drawing big willies, you'd be marched down to the Head to get your hands cut off.

But Sister Fay wasn't like other teachers. Not just because she was a nun. A nun who taught gym as well as RE. She was different because stuff that bugged other teachers didn't seem matter to her.

Like if you forgot your tie, or were eating in her RE class. Or you burped. She just let you get on with it.

Sister Fay only seemed to pick up on the good things about people. Not because she was soft. No. No. She'd run a mission before she came to St Mark's, and been in charge of a school and a hospital. There was no running water. Hardly any food. Far, far too many sick babies, she told us.

You could always tell by the way Sister Fay looked at you that she knew fine you were doing something wrong. She just chose to let most things go. Like Ben giving her lip. Sister Fay just chose not to listen to it.

"What's the beef with Mr P then?" Sister Fay patted Brad's baldy head on the poster. She smiled at us. One by one. Another thing about Sister Fay is that when she smiles, you can't help smiling back.

So instead of us just saying, "Nothing." Or *really* saying nothing and staring at the floor, like we do when other teachers want to know what's going on, I gave her a grin. And a shrug. The way Sister Fay looked you in the eye just made you tell the truth.

"We want make films, and Brad – I mean Mr Pitt – won't let us ..."

"... join his Club." Sister Fay cut in. She said the very words I was going to say myself.

"And he's got a top video camera we want to use," said Ben.

"What, that old thing?" Sister Fay cocked her head at Brad's door. Of course I thought the "old thing" she was talking about was Mr Comb-Over Brad Pitt.

I opened my mouth, ready to say, "Yeah, that fat, baldy old thing" when Sister Fay put her finger to my lips. Like she could read my mind. With her free hand she nipped the pen away from Ben before he could draw more curly hairs on Brad's willy.

"If you want to make films, then this is your lucky day. Jesus has heard your prayer." Sister Fay rubbed Brad's name-plate clean with her sleeve.

"Prayer?" Ben and Alan and I looked at each other. *Who's been praying?* I knew they were thinking.

Sister Fay smiled her smile. "Well, if He didn't hear yours, He heard mine." Sister Fay put her hands together and closed her eyes. "Thanks be," she said in a very holy voice. Then she opened one eye. Winked.

"So what the hell you hanging about out here for, growing old?" She lifted up her hands to Ben's cheeks and smacked him gently. "Join *my* Club, and you can go off with the brand new video doo-dah the school's given me."

"What?" I said.

"Club?" added Ben.

"New video camera?"

That was Alan. We were jogging to keep up with Sister Fay. Another thing about her is that she runs marathons to raise money for the missions all the time and moves faster than a greyhound chasing a rabbit.

"Thought you ran running club, Sister?" I puffed.

"And Go For Green." Sister Fay smiled. "I'm into saving my planet, you know."

"Go For Green?" panted Ben.

"Never heard of it," gasped Alan.

Sister Fay had stopped jogging. She smiled at Alan. "Well, now you have, pet. And you're so very welcome."

We were outside a drama room. There was a banner above it.

"**Go For Green Club**," the banner said. That was all. No daft posters of Sister Fay's face on Lady Gaga's body.

"Now," Sister Fay said as she shooed us into the room. "The Head's given me this." She handed me a box. On it was a picture of a hand holding a small video camera. The camera looked no bigger than a mobile phone.

Perfect! I thought.

Sister Fay nodded at me as if she could hear my thoughts. "So the Head's after a film about how we can all be more Green and still be happy. Three minutes long it's to be," she said.

Sister Fay gave us her biggest smile so far. "He's putting St Mark's into a film competition, and I can't even get this thing here out the box. So," she said, "d'you think I could leave you three smart kids to make me a movie?"

Chapter 5

Go For Green

"Pinch me."

That was Ben. Then he added, "This is ace!"

I thought his shaky hand was pointing to the neat, brand new video I was holding. But it wasn't, and he was shaking because he was in the same room as Polly Marr. Turns out she's a member of the "Go For Green Club." And when Ben walked in, Polly called over, "Hey, Ben. Welcome."

Poor Ben. He is so in love with Polly Marr he couldn't even say "Hey" back. He just sat and stared at her and shook like a new-born lamb. And this is the same guy who ate a worm and spider sandwich for a stunt the other day.

"Why did we never join Go For Green before?" Ben said in a shaky, baa-lamb voice. "It's got hot girls *and* a hot camera."

I bet Alan was thinking that too. But there was no way to check. He was busy in a tiny cupboard with Asha Latif. Asha had asked Alan if he fancied helping her sort out Sister Fay's used clothes pile.

By the sounds coming from the cupboard, all I think he was helping Asha do was giggle and squeak.

As for me, *I* was far too busy thinking about the film I could make to giggle or squeak with anyone.

"Man," I told Ben. Now we can do all those stunts we've planned. Jumping off roofs. Walking into walls. Hey," I went on, "you and Alan can dress up as old ladies. We can go down the shopping centre. You can pretend to drop dead. Then jump up when someone gives you the kiss of life. I'll film it all."

"Yeah, great kiss," said Ben. He sounded very keen. But he was gazing at Polly, not the video.

"And now you can push me along the side of the canal in a shopping trolley. Then tip me in. Alan's always wanted to film that. Sweet!" I tugged Ben's sleeve.

"Sweet," Ben said with a deep sigh. "The canal. It's so pretty."

"The *canal?* It's full of rats and rusty bikes. Are you *listening?*" I snapped my fingers at Ben's face.

"This camera works in the dark," I shook Ben's arms. "So we can hide in bushes at night. Jump out screaming at people. Bet we scare someone so bad they poo it. We'll film it all. Send it in to *Cray-Zee Stunts.*"

"I'd love to hide in a bush with Polly," Ben said in a dreamy voice. "Or get *her* on film. She's so pretty, Mel. Look at her planting seeds. Isn't she pretty?"

I gave up. While Ben stared at Polly, I spent the rest of lunchtime studying the camera manual.

"Grand to see you working away there, Mel," said Sister Fay when the bell rang. "I bet you'll have lots of great ideas for a Go For Green film."

"Oh, yes. Lots of ideas, Sister," I said.

Didn't I just?

For example, I'd been thinking about how I might sneak into the staff toilet next to Brad's classroom. I would cover the top of the pan with cling film. I would hide the video somewhere and leave it on "PLAY".

"Mel, you are so clever." Sister Fay sat down next to me. "Will you promise to make me a film that will make every pupil want to be more Green?" Sister Fay was looking deep into my eyes as she spoke. So I had to try and get rid of the picture in my head. It was of Brad with his trousers down. He was sitting on a toilet covered in cling film. There was a puddle of pee at his feet.

"Will you help me, Mel?" Sister Fay patted my hand before I could lie. "Ah, you will," she said. "You'll do me proud. I know I can trust you. You won't let me down."

Chapter 6
Mad Stunt Plans

"Can you believe we have our very own video – ?" said Ben.

" – to film our mad mental stunts," I said.

"Quick," said Alan. "Zoom in on this."

It was later that day. We were down the park. I was filming Alan's knee. He had a hot red boil right on the tip of it, and he was picking it with a twig.

"Squeeze ... Now!" I said, as Alan's boil went splat. It shot a jet of pus over the lens of the video.

"Did you film it?" Alan kept squeezing. The pus kept coming. And kept coming. The boil made me think of the lava from that volcano in Iceland. You know the one that stopped all the planes flying? The one that might erupt for years and years? Alan's knee looked like it could erupt for years too. And years.

"In the can." I high-fived Ben.

"What now?" he said. "I want to film us doing something proper sick and nuts."

"Like what?" I said. I was looking for something I could use to clean Alan's pus gunk off the camera. It was green. Looking at it made me feel sick. It also made me think of Sister Fay and her Go For Green Club.

How she said she knew she could trust us.

And that we'd do her proud.

How she'd given us a brand new video to make her a film.

And here we were, filming pus. I know it was green stuff, but this was not the kind of

Green stuff we *should* have been filming. What would Sister Fay say?

"Hey, you know what I feel like doing?" Ben was saying.

"'Chucking yourself at a fence?" said Alan. He was trying to film up his own nostrils.

"Nah. I was thinking we could sneak into the junk yard," said Ben.

"Good plan," said Alan. "Then film me kicking down a tower of car wrecks?"

"And Mel jumps clear before it goes CRASH!" said Ben.

"But we've done that," I said. "It just made a mega mess. *And* I got chased by that pit bull. It bit my butt."

"Skip-jumping then?" said Ben.

"I like it!" said Alan.

"But we've done that loads," I said.

"This time we could just *dive* in, head first." Ben dived at me and Alan to show us what he meant. We moved aside, so he stonked his head off the ground.

"Dangerous," I said. "People chuck glass and broken stuff in skips."

"Duh. That's the point. Stunt Dudes take chances," said Ben, rubbing his head. "So, let's dive a skip. And film it."

"Or," said Alan, "what about we *hide* in the skip till folk walk by. Then chuck rubbish at them."

"Hey, better still," Ben was having millions of mad skip ideas now. "Why don't we dive the skips round the back of the shopping centre? There's one just for McDonald's waste food."

"I like it!" nodded Alan. "We dive in. Come up with flies and maggots and left-over crap everywhere."

"We'll look like dead Big Macs walking."

"All cold fries and tomato sauce."

"We can run up to girls all mucky."

"Food dripping off us."

"Hug them."

"Count me out," I said. "I'm not hugging any girls!"

"We'll hug, you can film," Alan stood up. "So what we waiting for?" He put his fist to his chest.

"Let's do it ..." Alan began to say.

Ben was about to join in, but I held up my hand to stop him before it was too late.

I shook the video camera at Ben and Alan.

"We're not being very Go For Green, are we?" I said with a sigh.

"So?" said Ben.

Alan grabbed the video. "I only went along to that saddo Save the Stupid Planet Stupid Club to use this." He held the camera to my face and pressed the zoom in and out.

"It's Go For Green, not Save the Planet," I pushed Alan's hand away. "And you didn't think the Club was saddo while you were in that cupboard."

"Sorting smelly old clothes with Asha," Ben blew Alan a kiss.

"*You* didn't think it was saddo either." I poked Ben in the belly. "When you were staring at Polly. *'Oh yes, Polly. I'll be back next week.'*"

"What?" Alan shook his head at Ben. "You said we'd be going *back*? Forget that."

Ben's cheeks went bright red. "Alan's right. We don't do school clubs, Mel. We're Stunt Dudes." Ben was looking at me as he spoke, but I could tell his mind was somewhere else. He had his *goo-goo I love Polly* face on.

"But if we don't go back to Go For Green, Polly won't talk to you again. Ever," I told Ben. "You wouldn't like that."

Ben shook his head. "Polly's so pretty," he said.

"And if *we* don't go back to Go For Green," I told Alan, "Sister Fay'll take *this* back." I tapped the camera. "She needs a film for next week. And I promised her we'd make something about how you can be happy and have fun being Green."

"That's a stupid promise," said Alan. "We never do anything teachers want us to."

"But Sister Fay's not like other teachers. She's one of the good guys," I said.

"So what?" said Alan with a sneer.

"And if we don't make her film soon, she'll get someone else and give them the camera."

Alan said again, "Why waste time making a film about being Green?" He started walking away. "When we can make a film of us doing mad stunts *and* get on telly? Hey, are you coming to the scrap yard or not?" He cocked his head at me and Ben.

I stayed where I was. "Why can't we do the two things at once?" I asked.

"Huh?" Alan frowned at Ben.

I smiled. "Why can't we make a *stunt* film that's about being Green?"

"A stunt film about switching off lights, saving paper, making sure nothing's left on standby – " Alan yawned in my face.

"Hang on," I cut in. "That's the kind of Green film everyone *expects*." I punched my chest. "Not us. We can do something different."

40

"Like?" snapped Alan.

"Like a film about how you can be *happy* and have *fun* being Green," I said. "Think about it," I asked my pals. "What makes us happy?"

"Doing stunts and pranks," said Alan.

"And how do we have fun?" I asked again.

"Doing stunts and pranks." This time Ben joined with Alan.

"Well," I said, "we'll just make a stunt film. But keep it Green."

"And how do we do that?" asked Ben.

"And won't it end up really dull?" added Alan.

"Men, when have the Stunt Dudes ever been dull or boring?" I said. And I punched my chest. "Let's do it, dudes!"

Chapter 7
Skipping

The great thing about Ben and Alan is that once they say they'll do a thing, they never back down. Even if that thing is bonkers. Or ends one of them in A+E. Like the time we set 30 mouse traps. Then Ben took his clothes off, and rolled over them.

Ouch!! Ouch!! Ouch!!!

Please **DON'T** try *that* one at home, kids!

Unless you really love pain.

Or you don't feel it where most lads feel pain the most.

And like the idea of a mouse trap (or three) pinching that one place most lads feel pain the most …

Of course I knew a stunt like Ben's mouse-trap roll would be no good for Sister Fay's film. It had no message …

Well, that's not totally true. It had the message: *Don't catch your nuts in a mouse trap for laughs.* But it had no "Go For Green" message.

But Ben's skip idea did have a Go For Green message. It was a perfect place to start. People throw rubbish in skips. And as my mum likes to say, "One man's rubbish is another man's treasure."

So the next night we were round the back of the local shopping centre, in a dark alley. There was a row of open skips and massive wheelie bins all the way along it. They were for the shops to dump their rubbish in.

"But remember, we're not going to skip-dive," I hissed at Ben.

"Aw," said Alan and Ben together. "Where's the fun in being here, then?"

"Shh," I said. I was listening out for big evil security guards and their evil dogs. This would not be the first time we had come here at night and *those* dudes hated us.

"OK, you can skip-dive if you must," I whispered. "But I think we should be picking waste *out* the skip."

"Yeah. Like I said," said Alan. "To chuck at folk."

He was already pulling himself up the side of the biggest skip in the alley.

"Film me," he said. Then he tipped into the skip. All I could see were his legs sticking in the air like a pair of scissors wearing jeans and red Converse trainers.

"Hey! There's no one about to chuck anything at, dumbo," I hissed at him. "Why not pull rubbish out and we'll use it again for a stunt. We need that Go For Green message, remember?"

I tried to pull myself up the side of the skip. I was talking and holding the video at the same time. The skip was so high Ben gave me a leg up. Then he grabbed the camera and filmed me clinging on to the side of the skip. He was laughing so hard he couldn't keep his focus still.

"You want to see yourself, Mel. With your funny little short legs kicking in the air," Ben shook all over he was laughing so much.

"Help!" I panted, until Ben came to help. He grabbed my funny little short legs and pushed me over the top of the skip.

It was lucky for me there was a grotty old mattress to break my fall. Not so lucky for Alan. The grotty old mattress and me – we both fell on top of him.

"Gerroff me. This thing stinks," he said, as he crawled out. The mattress was wet and manky. Yuck.

"Well, we're not using *that* old thing for our film. No Green message there. It's done." I kicked the mattress. It oozed black gunk.

"Ugh!" I stepped away from it and my foot went from under me. Before I could grab the edge of the skip, I was falling and couldn't stop. The same way the spotty pants girl had fallen when her foot went over that pencil in Brad's class. Only I didn't end up on my back. Something stopped me falling too far.

"Oopla!" Ben shouted. He videoed me as I lost my balance.

"Mel, you're a total stunt star!" he hooted. Ben was in the skip too now, picking his way over to me. "Could you not wait till you got home, Mel?" he said. He moved the camera down to film what I'd landed on.

A toilet pan.

I was sitting on an old toilet. Or rather, I was sitting *in* it.

"Yikes!" I jumped up. But my foot slipped. And there I was stuck in the pan again.

"This is all in the can," hooted Ben. He pointed at the old toilet. "Can? Toilet. You're in the can. Geddit? Oh, Mel. You wanna see your face."

Ben was playing back his film. Alan climbed over the junk in the skip to watch. He was lugging a massive toy panda. The head was hanging off and all the stuffing was falling out the neck.

"Do you think we can use this old thing?" Alan flung the panda at me. "He's as tubby as Brad and as big as you, Mel." The panda doofed me on the back of the head.

"Oi, watch it!" I said. I was feeling round my feet, trying to find the thing that had made me fall over.

"And check this out. Wow!" I gasped, holding up a skate-board. One end of the deck was broken off, but all the trucks were still there. Worn, but turning.

"This is too good!" I grinned at my pals.

"You said it, Mel." Ben was filming again. "You've a giant panda on your head and you're stuck down a toilet in a skip waving a broken skate-board."

"It's Go For Green gold," agreed Alan.

"Not yet. But at least we've some props now."

I took the video from Ben and chucked the panda over the side of the skip. "We'll take Brad the Panda. And this." I tucked the skate-board under my arm. Then I climbed out the skip.

"What are you waiting for? Send the toilet down to me." I grinned up to Ben and Alan. "Then let's make a movie."

Chapter 8
Who Goes There?

We made our way out the lane with the stuff we'd found in the skip. I had the old skate-board under one arm and Brad the giant panda under the other. He was tricky to carry – floppy and clumsy – but Alan and Ben had the real problem. They were carting the old toilet.

We only made it as far as the wheelie bins.

"Phew. Heavy work, this," Alan let his side of the toilet drop to the ground with a clunk. Then he plonked on the seat to get his breath back. "Why don't you just film me on the pan here?" said Alan. "Then we'll dump it back in the skip."

"No!" I said.

"But this toilet's so heavy, Mel." Alan groaned. "What are we even going to do with it? It's not like you know what your film's going to be about yet."

Alan moved his butt into the middle of the toilet. "While you're thinking I'll kid on I need a mega crap."

"What's Go For Green about *that*?" I asked. But Alan had already started doing his on-the-toilet noises. Alan loves doing them. Ben loves Alan doing his on-the-toilet noises too.

"This isn't 'Go For Green'," it's 'Go For a Crap," Ben snorted behind the camera as Alan grunted, "Ooooh! Ahhhhh! Haaaaa!" and pulled mad on–the-toilet faces to match his sound-effects.

I knew this was not a film I could ever give Sister Fay, but I couldn't help laughing. Alan is one funny dude. He was making his eyes water and his cheeks puff out, fat and red.

"You know who you look like?" I hooted. I walked the giant panda up to the toilet pan and shoved him on it behind Alan.

"*Ooooh! Ahhhhh! Haaaaa, my friend!*" I made my own on-the-toilet noises. "You're like Brad when he's mad."

"Or taking a crap." That was Ben. "I bet this is what he looks like."

"Oh, hang on a minute, dudes. Now we're talking." Alan stood up. He set the panda on the pan where he'd been sitting.

"Recycled toilet, recycled toy called Brad," Alan said. "You're right, Mel. We can make a stunt film using these props. We've even got our own film star."

"All we need is a bit of a story," I said as Ben and Alan lifted the toilet and Brad the Panda on to the skate-board.

"And it's gotta be an action movie." Alan shoved the skate-board with his foot. The old trucks rolled along the alley as far as the last wheelie bin.

"Look at Brad taking a dump!" I ran after the skate-board. The idea was so funny, I forgot to keep my voice down. I was yelling.

Alan was the same. "Hey, let's dress Brad the Panda up like a geography teacher," Alan's voice boomed.

"Hey! Great idea. We'll get the Silver Sisters to help," Ben shouted louder than me or Alan.

And at that moment someone stepped out from the side of the last wheelie bin. The person took aim then threw an empty burger box at Ben.

"You trying to get us all arrested?" snapped a woman's voice.

And I froze. I knew that voice.

Chapter 9

Freegans

"Sister Fay?" I gasped.

"Who's asking?"

It was so dark in the alley, the person I *thought* might be Sister Fay was just a black shape in front of me.

"It's Mel," I said. "And Ben. And Alan."

"Friends not foe, then," came the smiley voice that told me the black shape *was* Sister Fay. "But what on earth," she started to sound less smiley, "are you doing down an alley at this time of night?"

I was just going to say *"Making our film for you"* when Alan snorted, "What are we doing out here, Sister Fay? What are *you* doing here?"

"Shhh. Would you keep the voice down and I'll show you," Sister Fay whispered.

She flicked on a small torch. It lit up the great big bin beside us. The lid was open, and there a head was sticking out. Was it a man or a woman? Was it even a human? I couldn't tell. The head wore a big woolly hat, and there was a scarf over the mouth and nose. All you could see was the glitter of two eyes.

"Woody," said Sister Fay to the head in the bin. "Here's the pals I told you about. The ones making a Green film for me." Sister Fay flashed the torch about and I saw she was dressed the same as Woody – woolly hat, scarf over her face, and overalls.

"Mhhhh," nodded the head as its hand came out the skip. It was wearing a thick rubber glove like the one my dad uses to clear drains. I went to shake it, but Sister Fay blocked me.

"I wouldn't touch. We wear the mitts in case of rats, or needles." Sister Fay pointed out her own thick glove.

"But why?" Alan and I asked at the same time. We were watching as Woody slung a black bin-bag out the bin.

"There's why." Sister Fay flashed her torch into the bin bag. It was full of food.

"Apples. Bread. Ready-meals. Oh, look. And four steaks. All going to waste. Me and Woody make sure it doesn't."

"You mean you take it?" I asked.

"Is that not stealing?" This was Alan.

"It's shocking. A sin, that's what it is! People are starving and this food's in a bin and still fit to eat," said Sister Fay. There was no smiling in her tone any more.

"Amen! A bloody sin." This comment came from Woody. *Hey. And she's a woman too,* I thought to myself as soon as I heard Woody's voice. Sister Fay went on, "While the other nuns in the convent are watching *Eastenders,* me and Woody here slip out. Pick out anything from the bins that's still safe to eat – "

" – but that the shops won't sell," Woody added.

" – because it's just gone out of date." Woody showed me a tub of yogurt that was fresh till today.

"Or maybe the wrapper's torn. Look!" Sister Fay held out a packet of muffins.

"Go on," she nodded till I took one. "Dig in! See? Nothing wrong with these, is there?"

"Apart from the waste," said Woody. "That's why we do this. We're Freegans. Trying to live off free food no one wants."

Woody was climbing out of the bin. She was a bit slow and stiff, I saw. Sister Fay grabbed her hands and helped get her down to the ground. Then she passed Woody a walking stick.

"Oh, that was fun, Fay. Keeps me young," Woody puffed. "Tiring, but fun."

Woody pulled off her woolly hat, tugged down her thick scarf. And now Ben and Alan and I were looking at a tiny old lady. She'd wrinkles and white hair and a hearing aid.

"You're eco-nuns!" This was Alan.

"Go For Green Nuns!" I chipped in.

"Go For Green Stunt Nuns!" Ben added, from behind the camera.

"Go For Green Eco-Stunt Nuns. I do like that," Woody said with a giggle as she picked up her bin bag of Freegan food and limped off with her stick.

"So you really eat this stuff?" I asked.

"Some of it," said Sister Fay. "We give most of it away."

"No one knows it comes from the back of a supermarket and not the inside," Woody called.

"The money we save on food bills goes to good causes instead," Sister Fay picked up her own Freegan goodies.

"Now don't you lot be hanging about," she said as she walked away. "You never know what crazy nutters you're going to meet down this lane. Night, night. God Bless."

"Wow! How cool was that? They so have to be in our film!" said Alan when we couldn't see Sister Fay or Woody any more.

"They have to be the stars!" That was me.

We wheeled Brad the Panda and the old toilet back to my house on the skate-board. "Too right, Stunt Nuns have got to be in the film," said Ben. He played his footage of Sister Fay and Woody in their mad woolly hats on my computer. "Woody's head poking out the bin is so funny."

"Not as funny as when she pulls off her hat, and there's this old lady," I said.

"Old *nun*. Climbing out a *bin*. It's madder than anything on *Cray-Zee Stunts*," said Alan.

"The Stunt Sisters. It's cool too. And funny but not funny," I said. "I mean, Woody and Fay don't just talk about being Green." I punched my heart. "They're the real deal."

"So we all agree? The eco-nuns star in our film?"

We all nodded.

"So let's do it! Do it, dudes!"

Chapter 10
Cheap Thrills – The Movie

Yay! At Last. Time to make the movie.

First of all we made some calls.

Alan rang Asha. He asked if she fancied being our Wardrobe Mistress. When she said, "Oooh! Love to!" he asked her to bring over some of the old clothes from Sister Fay's Go For Green cupboard.

I rang the Silver Sisters. When I said, "Would you like to style us for a film?" Jasper and Robbie's screams were so shrill down my mobile, I had swap to text: "Cn u do our make-up 2?"

I'd have been deaf if I'd *asked* them over the phone. They were still screaming when they arrived at my house with their sketch pads. Plus more make-up than my mum and two sisters own between them. And that is a *lot* of make-up, let me tell you!

Ben said he'd ask Polly to help us. He begged Asha for Polly's mobile number. But then he lost his bottle. Ben is such a big soft lump that his hand shook so much he couldn't even *text* her.

So I sent Ben back to the food skip in the lane with two bin bags. I told him to fill them with food that was too spoilt for Freegans to eat. While he was away, *I* texted Polly

"Do u wnt 2 make film with Ben?"

"!!!! ☺" she texted back.

Polly's job was to bring plastic bags. While we waited for her and Ben to come over, the rest of us got busy turning Brad the Panda into a film star. First Asha sewed his head back on, then she clipped most of the fur off the top of his head so he looked as baldy as Mr Brad. Then the Silver Sisters got to work. They dressed the panda in a grotty yellow shirt and ugly tie and nasty brown geography teacher trousers. All from the local charity shop. I found a picture of the real Brad Pitt and stapled it over Brad the Panda's face. We sat him in the toilet on the broken skate-board.

Then Asha and the Silver Sisters dressed me and Alan in mad outfits from the Go For Green clothes pile. Alan wore a pink ball gown and cowboy hat. I was in a mini-skirt and frilly top and a long curly wig. We found a boob tube for Ben, and some tiny denim shorts. We were dressed to kill. With the camera rolling the Stunt Dudes, that's us, plus Asha and Polly and the Silver Sisters pushed Brad the Panda to the steepest hill in the park.

We took all Polly's plastic bags and tied them together to make a long slippy slide. We laid the slide on the hill and then we sent Brad the Panda on his toilet pan down. As he rolled, we all stood at the side of the slide and pelted him with the food from the skip. And Ben filmed, of course.

Then it was the Stunt Dudes' turn to get dirty. One by one we sat on the old toilet and flew down the hill on the skate-board. Cray-Zee Stunt-style, of course. First Ben lay flat on the top of the pan. He flew down head first shouting "Nyyyyawwww," till he landed in the duck pond.

I went next. Dressed up as Miss Wiggle, thanks to the Silver Sisters. I lay on my back across the pan and took Brad the Panda with me. We hugged and kissed all the way down the hill. Till the pan fell off the skate-board. And we rolled into a puddle.

Alan went last, in his pink ball gown. He stuck his head right down the toilet pan and did a handstand on the skate-board. And he made it all the way down, with the girls and the Silver Sisters and me chucking rotten eggs and squishy tomatoes at him.

By this time a crowd of people had stopped to watch. They clapped and cheered till a pair of park keepers on walkie-talkies came running up to see what the noise was about.

Before the parkies asked us to leave, we scooped up all the food mess we had thrown, put it back in the bin bags, and split.

The camera had run out of battery anyway.

Chapter 11
The End

We ended up with a film of two halves.

In the first half, we speeded up me and Alan and Ben and Brad the Panda rolling down the hill in the park. We set the action to crazy *deedly-deedly* banjo music. We called it "**Cheap Thrills – Part One**" and flashed up messages on the screen.

No geography teachers were harmed while making this film

said the first message.

The second one was in bright green letters. It said:

And what you see comes for **Free**

Same as this

Then came "**Cheap Thrills – Part Two.**"

We ran this part of the film in slow motion, and let it play with no soundtrack.

Can you guess what it showed?

Yup.

Just two shapes. In mad gear. In an alley. Filling two bin bags with waste food from a skip.

Is there anything funny about this?????

It said along the bottom of the screen.

And do you know what? "**Cheap Thrills – The Movie**" won that Green film competition.

The judges said it was clever yet shocking, and funny, and made you think about how much gets thrown away.

The day after we won, the Head called me and Ben and Alan up on stage in front of the whole school. The last time that happened, it was because we'd taken turns to push each other off the roof of the gym on to an air bed.

That time, the Head told us we were a disgrace and the sooner we were his ex-pupils, the better.

This time he told us we should be very proud indeed.

"Hear, hear," agreed Sister Fay. Then she played our film in Assembly.

And, oh boy! Did it go down well?

During **Part 1** there was stamping and clapping and cheering. Especially for Brad the Panda. While I was rolling down the hill, dressed up like Miss Wiggle and kissing Brad, the whole school wolf-whistled and shouted "*Ooh, la, la!*" And Mr Brad the geography teacher sat with his arms crossed, and his head tucked into his chins.

During **Part 2** there was a gasp when the torch flashed on the face of one of the shapes in the woolly hat, and pupils saw that it was Sister Fay. There was silence till the film was over.

But Sister Fay was mobbed after Assembly. A lot of the pupils wanted to join her Go For Green Club to try crazy stunts with rubbish. But even more wanted Sister Fay to take them on Freegan missions.

"Result," Ben and Alan and I nodded to each other. "We've made people smile and think, and we've had a blast doing it." As we walked away with the Silver Sisters and Asha and Polly, Brad stopped us.

"Well done there, my friends," he said. "You'd be most welcome in Film Club if you've nothing better to do at lunchtimes."

Alan looked at Asha and Ben looked at Polly (and went bright, bright red, of course).

I looked at the Silver Sisters, and they blew kisses at the vintage skirt they'd made me wear for Assembly. (Well, who says Stunt Dudes have to be boys?)

"Thanks, Sir," I spoke for all of us. "But to be honest, I think we'd rather Go For Green."

Barrington Stoke would like to thank all its readers for commenting on the manuscript before publication and in particular:

Thomas Barrett
Holly Bennett
Sophie Boswell
Jamie Bouwer
Rosy Briggs
Stephanie Buchanan
Julie Carss
Parasha Collins
Tony Collins
Alex Costin
Patrick De Waard
Charlie Dingle
Lauren Ditcher
Rory Donoghoe
Tyler Eastlake
Jemma Grayson
Scarlet Hackfield
Daniel Hogan
Aaron Hutch
Eoin Ivory
Jordan Kearns

Alex Keyworth
Penny Konig
Martin Leavy
Gavin Maher
Alwyn Martin
Elton McArdle
Sean McDermott
David McDonagh
Hughie McDonagh
Joshua Miyake
James Morgan
Ciaran O' Doherty
Simon O' Donnell
Evan O' Shea
Ryan Pearce
Hannah Sharp
Ben Trembath
Hedley Trenerry
Amy Walker
Alan Wright